GOOD HOUSEKEEPING
FAVORITE WEIGHT-LOSS RECIPES

Text edited for the Good Housekeeping Institute by Linda Webb.

Graphic design and illustration by Mary Sealfon.

ISBN 0-87851-125-3

HOW TO USE THIS BOOK

An essential part of healthy living is weight control. And, here for men and women who want to lose excess pounds, is a sensible and effective dieting plan with a wide variety of food choices. To correct over-eating patterns, you will fill out a diet diary plus learn about behavior modification tips that will help you develop a no-gain eating style. Plus, there are two weeks of low-calorie menus you can follow; then, plan you own weekly menus and choose selected low-calorie recipes in the second part of the book. Or, use these delicious recipes for simply keeping you and your family trim by avoiding unnecessary extra calories.

CONTENTS

CHAPTER 1

EATING TO LOSE WEIGHT

Chances are by now you've experienced the typical weight reducing cycle that goes like this: you painstakingly lose the desired number of pounds, gradually return to the kind of thoughtless eating that caused the original weight gain, watch the needle on the scale go up—and start all over again.

The key to breaking out of this discouraging cycle is in identifying and correcting the eating habits that cause the problem; and at the same time, following a sensible eating plan. A plan which offers a variety of food choices and is safely calorie controlled, but not drastically reduced, so that weight loss is gradual and therefore effective (which means pounds *stay off*) as well as medically safe. A gradual weight loss also allows you the necessary time to become familiar with your new way of eating.

Learning how to change your eating habits is probably the greatest benefit you'll get from the weight-reducing plan in this book. How you handle food is the factor which determines whether you'll

stay slim or gain unwanted pounds. In developing skills which put you in control of food, you'll bypass traps to overeating so that less willpower to resist food will be required. And, once at your goal, maintaining your trim waistline will become second nature to you.

So, begin now by following the positive steps outlined below to developing your new way of eating and use the eating plans for men and women starting on the following pages as your guidelines for a nutritionally balanced and safely calorie-controlled weight reducing diet.

Steps to Developing Your No-Gain Eating Pattern

Begin by keeping a written record, an actual "diet diary" as shown right. By making notes on when, where and what you eat, as well as on the accompanying persoual circumstances, you will develop a personal, and valuable food-intake profile. At the end of a week take a good look at the diary and analyze the information you've gathered. See a pattern? You should be able to pinpoint the situations in which you overeat.

At this point, you're ready to revise, though not necessarily change, your eating patterns. In some cases, it's possible to keep a habit—late night snacking, for example—as long as you adjust total calorie intake to accommodate it. With other habits, it may be necessary to find mind-over-matter ways to wean yourself away. Here are some examples of problems you might encounter and how you can deal with them.

"Whenever I see food, I have to eat." But are you really hungry? At times, just stopping to think about whether or not you're hungry is enough to help you say "No," then turn your back on the temptation.

Remember, too, "out of sight, out of mind." Be sure all your food is kept in cabinets or in the refrigerator, where it won't catch your eye.

"My worst snack-craving is at night". Plan ahead. If you know your hunger-pang pattern calls for evening treats, save up calories. For instance, skip a serving of bread and/or fruit at dinner so you can enjoy it later on. Prepare raw vegetables ahead of time to have on hand for mid-evening munching. Choose snacks that take a long time to eat—small crackers, grapes and the like.

"I have trouble sticking to a diet plan when I go out to eat". Choose a restaurant where you know the menu includes foods you can eat without feeling guilty. Avoid extras. Don't hesitate to ask that your meat or fish be prepared without sauces or extra butter. Have your salad dressing served on the side. If the entree comes with accompaniments that are off-limits, ask the waiter not to serve them to you. You don't have to skip dessert —order fresh fruit.

"I eat a meal in less than 10 minutes." When you eat too fast, your body doesn't have time to signal that you're full and you may have second portions and dessert before realizing you weren't even that hungry. Slow down. Let the signals work, and listen to them. Start with a filling but low-calorie appetizer, like soup. Serve dinner in separate courses: soup, then salad, then the main dish. Put your fork down between bites. Chew thoroughly. Finish with coffee or tea and then decide if you really need desert.

"I eat any time, any place, anything whether I'm hungry or not." Ask yourself before eating: Am I hungry? Do I really want to eat or am I eating because the food is there? Would I prefer to eat something else? Knowing you're not hungry, or deciding the food is not that appealing, may be enough to help you say "no thanks". Eat only when hungry, and only food you enjoy. Many successful dieters become gourmets.

"When I 'go off' my diet, I feel so guilty that I give up." What is not so obvious here is that the negative feeling of guilt, not the actual act of "going off the diet", is what keeps you from successfully losing weight. Guilt breeds hopelessness — a real trap to overeating. If you cheat, don't dwell on it. Take a positive step forward and continue with your diet where you left off. Remember, one bad hour does not make a bad day. Concentrate on your successes only. And, just a tip to keep in mind if a food seems absolutely irresistible and you start to "dig in"—the first and last bite always taste the same.

A Weight Reducing Plan That Works

How much should you weigh?
Naturally, before starting a diet, you need to know what your goal-weight will be. As a rule of thumb, the weight that is desirable for you when you are in your mid-twenties is considered the best weight for later years. You can get an idea of what your desirable weight might be by using the weight table on the following page.

Setting Your Goals
Be realistic about your goal setting. Avoid developing an attitude such as you're going to lose five pounds in a week or else. You're only creating a potential for frustration later on since your body does not recognize time as a determinant for shedding pounds. What it recognizes is when energy needs are not being met over a period of time by the calories provided in foods. Body fat must then be taken out of storage for fuel. Since one pound of body fat represents 3500 calories, to lose one pound, you must eat 3500 calories less than your body requires for energy, burn up 3500 extra calories through physical exercise, or preferably both by eating less *and* exercising more. This puts your body in a state of negative calorie balance. The time it takes to create a steady caloric deficit, and the rate at which stored fat is used for energy, will depend on you and your lifestyle. But, a reasonable rate of weight loss (mostly body fat) is one to two pounds a week.

MY DIET DIARY						
Time of day	Where was food eaten?	Was I hungry?	What else was I doing?	Who was with me?	What was eaten? How much?	How was I feeling?
7:30	Kitchen	yes	nothing	Children	1/2 cup juice, 1/2 cup cereal, 1/2 cup milk	neutral
10:30	living room	no	watching T.V.	alone	donut & coffee	tired

Be sure to weigh yourself only once a week, on the same scale, same place. Your weight may fluctuate, but that's a normal process often caused by fluid retention. Just concentrate on following the diet plan and the success you're having at avoiding traps to overeating with your new eating habits. You *will* lose weight.

If you plan to lose more than ten pounds, check with your doctor first. In fact, it might be just around the time when you're having that important yearly medical check-up.

The Importance of Physical Activity

Any form of physical activity—walking, calisthenics, dancing, swimming, etc.—is an essential component of a weight-reducing plan. Exercise is the way to burn extra calories and simultaneously maintain your body in healthy physical condition. Being involved in a physical activity is also an excellent technique to avoid eating, and after exercising, you'll not only feel terrific, but you'll be *less* hungry, too! Plus, exercising while losing weight helps to minimize the amount of lean body mass (muscle tissue) which is inevitably lost when you reduce calories. Overall, you'll lose the same amount of body weight, but the proportion of fat lost to lean body mass loss will be greater than if you didn't exercise. So, it's important to start walking to work, climbing stairs, parking at the far end of the parking lot or using any other inventive means you can think of to keep your body in motion. Every movement counts.

THE WEIGHT-REDUCING EATING PLANS

The Weight-Reducing eating plans below are nutritionally balanced and provide 1200 calories a day for women and 1800 for men—sensible and effective calories for long-term reducing. There are enormous variety of foods to choose from, so you can adapt the diet to your food preferences.

Listed on the next page are food choices, each with the recommended serving size. Foods with

Weights of Persons 20 to 30 Years Old

Height (without shoes)	Low Pounds	Average Pounds	High Pounds
Men			
5 feet 3 inches	118	129	141
5 feet 4 inches	122	133	145
5 feet 5 inches	126	137	149
5 feet 6 inches	130	142	155
5 feet 7 inches	134	147	161
5 feet 8 inches	139	151	166
5 feet 9 inches	143	155	170
5 feet 10 inches	147	159	174
5 feet 11 inches	150	163	178
6 feet	154	167	183
6 feet 1 inch	158	171	188
6 feet 2 inches	162	175	192
6 feet 3 inches	165	178	195
Women			
5 feet	100	109	118
5 feet 1 inch	104	112	121
5 feet 2 inches	107	115	125
5 feet 3 inches	110	118	128
5 feet 4 inches	113	122	132
5 feet 5 inches	116	125	135
5 feet 6 inches	120	129	139
5 feet 7 inches	123	132	142
5 feet 8 inches	126	136	146
5 feet 9 inches	130	140	151
5 feet 10 inches	133	144	156
5 feet 11 inches	137	148	161
6 feet	141	152	166

Weight Reducing Eating Plans

Food Groups		Women	Men
FOR THE DAY	Calories:	1200	1800
		servings	
meat and protein-rich foods		2	3
fruits and vegetables			
fruits		3	4
vegetables		2 to 4	2 to 4
breads, cereals, pastas,			
some vegetables		4	7
milk and milk products		2	2
extras		3	6
SUGGESTED MEAL PLANS			
Breakfast			
fruit		1	1
bread, cereals, etc.		1	3
meat and protein-rich foods		*	*
milk and milk products		1	1
extras		1	2
Lunch or supper			
meat and protein-rich foods		1*	1*
vegetables		1 to 2	1 to 2
breads, cereals, etc.		2	2
fruit		1	1
milk and milk products		1	1
extras		1	2
Dinner			
meal and protein-rich foods		1	2
vegetables		1 to 2	1 to 2
bread, cereals, etc.		1	2
fruit		1	2
extras		1	2

At each meal, if you wish coffee or tea with little or no sugar, with milk rather than cream.

*If one egg is eaten at breakfast, decrease luncheon serving of meat by one third.

similiar nutrients are categorized into food groups; therefore, foods within a group can be interchanged. Do not, however, substitute foods from one group to another.

The weight reducing eating plans list total servings allowed from each group everyday. The menu outlines are practical ways to distribute the servings among three meals. These are only guides however. You might like to arrange your menu differently to save servings of foods for planned snacks, or to have extra portions for dining out. As long as you include

daily the number of servings listed for each group in the recommended amounts, your diet will be nutritionally balanced* and calorie-controlled. If a specific food you want isn't listed, assign it to the category with foods it's most like. On the next two pages are suggested menu plans which include recipes in this book.

*Since it is difficult to fit practically a woman's full iron requirement (18 milligrams daily) within a 1200-calorie limit, it makes sense to eat one of the fortified breakfast cereals or to use an iron supplement or balanced vitamin- and -iron supplement.

Select Your Favorite Foods

MEAT AND PROTEIN-RICH FOODS

Cheese
cottage,* farmer's, pot or ricotta, ½ cup
American, Cheddar, Edam, Swiss, etc.,† 3 ounces
Eggs (3 medium)
Fish and shellfish
cooked bass,* bluefish, cod,* flounder,* haddock,* halibut, herring (plain), lobster,* mackerel, ocean perch, sole,* swordfish, trout, etc., 4 ounces
medium shrimp, 6
medium clams or oysters,* 10
crab,* salmon or tuna, 4 ounces flaked, drained
Legumes, 6 ounces cooked
Meat
cooked beef, game meats,* lamb, liver (all kinds),* pork, rabbit* or veal,* 3 ounces
boiled ham or lean luncheon meat,† 3 ounces
frankfurters,† 3 small
Peanut butter (⅓ cup†)
Poultry
cooked chicken,* Cornish hens, duck,† goose† or turkey, 4 ounces

*comparatively low in calories; use them often.
†Comparatively high in calories, use them sparingly.

BREADS, CEREALS, PASTAS, SOME VEGETABLES

Breads
rye, white and whole-wheat, 1 slice
matzoh, 1 piece*
raisin, 1 slice*
Cereals
flaked or puffed ready-to-eat, or cooked, 1 ounce dry weight, check label for serving size
Crackers
graham, 2 small
oyster, ½ cup
round, 5 2-inch
rye, 3 double crackers
saltines, 4 2-inch
soda, 3 small

Pastas
cooked macaroni, spaghetti, ⅔ cup
cooked egg noodles, ½ cup
Quick breads
biscuits, 1 average*
corn bread, 1½-inch cube*
English muffins, ½ muffin
pancakes, 1 4-inch cake*
muffins, 1 average*
waffles, 1 4-inch waffle*
Rice
cooked white, brown, or wild, ½ cup
Rolls
large hamburger, hot dog, etc., ½ roll
Vegetables
beets, 1 cup
corn, ⅓ cup
onions, raw, 1 cup
peas, green, 1 cup
potatoes, white, boiled or mashed, 1 cup; baked, 1 small
potatoes, sweet, baked, 1 small
rutabagas, 1 cup
turnips, 1 cup
winter squash, 1 cup

*Count as 1 serving of Bread and 1 serving of Extras

FRUITS AND VEGETABLES

Fruits, fresh, reduced calorie canned or frozen

apple, 1 small
apple juice, ⅓ cup
applesauce, ½ cup
apricots, 2 medium
banana, ½ small
berries, ⅔ to 1 cup
cantaloupe, ¼ small
cherries, 10 large
dates, 2 small
figs, fresh, 2 large
grapefruit, ½ small
grapefruit juice, ½ cup
grape juice, ¼ cup
grapes, 12 medium
honeydew, ⅛ small
mango, ½ small
orange, 1 medium
orange juice, ½ cup

papaya, ⅓ medium
peach, 1 medium
pear, 1 small
pineapple cubed, ½ cup
pineapple juice, ⅓ cup
plums or prunes, 2 medium
raisins, 2 tablespoons
tangerine, 1 large
tangerine juice, ½ cup
watermelon, cubed, 1 cup

Vegetables—use them freely on diet, served unbuttered or with low-calorie dressing

asparagus	lettuce
broccoli	mushrooms
Brussels	okra
sprouts	peppers
cabbage	radishes
carrot	romaine
cauliflower	sauerkraut
celery	spinach
cucumbers	summer
escarole	squash
green beans	tomato juice
greens	tomatoes
Italian beans	wax beans
kale	zucchini

MILK AND MILK PRODUCTS

Buttermilk, 1 cup
Cheese, American, Cheddar, etc., 1 ounce
Cottage cheese (creamed), ½ cup
Evaporated skimmed milk (undiluted), ½ cup
Nonfat dry milk powder, ⅓ cup
Skimmed milk, 1 cup
Yogurt, plain, ½ cup

THE EXTRAS

butter, 1 teaspoon
cream, sour, 2 tablespoons†
cream cheese, 1 tablespoon†
margarine, 1 teaspoon
plain popcorn, ⅔ cup†
pretzels, 10 sticks†
salad dressing, 2 teaspoons
sugar, 2 teaspoons*
vegetable oil, 1 teaspoon

*Limit to once per day
†Use occasionally

Sunday

LOW CALORIE

Orange Juice
Ready-to-Eat Cereal
Skimmed Milk
Coffee or Tea

•

Grilled Cheese on Rye Bread
Stewed Tomatoes
Tossed Salad
Club Soda with Lemon

•

Fish Fillets with Herb
Lemon Topping*
Fluffy Rice
Asparagus Spears
Peach Parfait*

Monday

½ Grapefruit
Whole Wheat Toast
Cottage Cheese
Coffee or Tea

•

Tuna Salad Sandwich
Carrot Sticks
Baked Apple
Skimmed Milk

•

Chicken "Manicotti*"
Spaghetti   Zucchini Slices
Mixed Green Salad
Fresh Orange

Tuesday

Tomato Juice
Oatmeal with Raisins
Skimmed Milk

•

Sliced Chicken Sandwich with
Tomato and Lettuce
Marinated Vegetables*
Canteloupe

•

Old Fashion Beef Stew*
Tossed Salad
Pineapple Chunks
Coffee or Tea

Wednesday

Orange Juice
Bran Muffin
Cottage Cheese
Coffee or Tea

•

Herbed Vegetable Soup*
Tomato Stuffed with Tuna
Saltines   Butter
Fruit Cocktail

•

Sliced Steak Au Jus*
Whipped Potato
Peas and Carrots
Tossed Salad Greens
Blueberries

Thursday

Tomato Juice
Ready-to-Eat Cereal
Banana Slices
Skimmed Milk

•

Hamburger on Bun
Lettuce and Tomato
Cole Slaw
Fresh Pear

•

Spicy Chicken with Yogurt*
Fluffy Rice   Green Beans
Canned Peaches
Coffee or Tea

Friday

Fresh Orange
Scrambled Egg
Buttered Toast
Coffee or Tea

•

Cottage Cheese with Pineapple
Chunks on Lettuce
Whole Wheat Bread
Skimmed Milk

•

Easy Baked Pork Chops*
Buttered Noodles
Brussels Sprouts
Applesauce
Ice Milk

Saturday

Grapefruit Sections
American Cheese
Rye Toast
Coffee or Tea

•

Frankfurter on Roll
Cole Slaw
Fresh Grapes
Skimmed Milk

•

Skillet Ham and Potatoes*
Broccoli Spears
Tossed Garden Salad
Fresh Orange

*See receipes pages 10-46

14-DAY MENUS

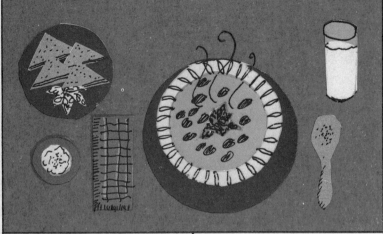

Sunday

Pancakes (two 4-inch)
topped with applesauce
Skimmed Milk

•

Gazpacho Cheese Salad*
Carrot Sticks
Corn Muffin   Butter
Sliced Strawberries

•

Pot Roast with Sauerkraut
and Carrots*
Buttered Noodles
Fresh apple
Coffee or Tea

Monday

Orange Juice
Ready-to-Eat Cereal
Skimmed Milk
Coffee or Tea

•

Omlette filled with chopped
Vegetables
Lettuce and Tomato
English Muffin
Canned Apricots

•

Chinese Chicken Rolls*
Fluffy Rice   Spinach
Applesauce
Coffee or Tea

Tuesday

Sliced Strawberries
Swiss Cheese
Whole Wheat Toast
Coffee or Tea

•

Chef's Salad
Small hard roll
Butter
Baked Apple
Club Soda

•

Pouched Flounder
Mediterranean*
Buttered Rice
Tossed Salad
Canned Pears
Graham Crackers

Wednesday

Tomato Juice
Hot Cereal with Raisins
Skimmed Milk
Coffee or Tea

•

Old Fashioned Beet Soup*
Egg Salad on Lettuce Hero*
Refrigerated Biscuit
Butter
Fresh Orange

•

Round Steak Diablo*
Buttered Noodles
Corn
Canned Peaches
Coffee or Tea

Thursday

½ Grapefruit
English Muffin
Skimmed Milk

•

Spinach Salad with Ham and
Fresh Mushrooms
Whole Wheat Toast
Baked Apple
Coffee or Tea

•

Turkey Cutlets in
Mushroom Sauce*
Baked Potato
Asparagus Spears
Canned Plums
Coffee or Tea

Friday

Tomato Juice
Ready-to-Eat Cereal
Banana Slices
Skimmed Milk

•

Beef Bouillon
Chicken Salad Sandwich
Cucumber Sticks
Pineapple Slices

•

Mock Beef Stroganoff*
Buttered Noodles
Green Beans
½ Grapefruit
Coffee or Tea

Saturday

Orange Juice
Small Hard Roll
Cottage Cheese
Coffee or Tea

•

Luncheon Meat Sandwich
Carrot and Celery Sticks
Ice Milk

•

Chicken Breast with Carrot
and Zucchini Stuffing*
Whipped Potato
Tossed Salad
Pineapple Slices

CHAPTER 2

LOW CALORIE RECIPES

The low-calorie recipes in this section can be used as part of the Weight-Loss Diet Plan for Men and Women or for simply keeping trim by reducing extra unnecessary calories

All the recipes have been developed, tested and tasted many times in the Good Housekeeping Institute kitchens. To ensure success, read the recipe before you begin and follow instructions precisely using the exact amount of ingredients as specified.

This is important for any recipe and critical in low-calorie recipes—extra dabs of butter here and there can add extra hundreds of calories.

Calories per serving (rounded to the nearest 5 calories) are given for each recipe. They've been determined by using publications issued by the U.S. Department of Agriculture and data submitted by food manufacturers.

To locate recipes use index below.

MAIN DISHES

Stir-Fried
Vegetable Mix

Deviled
Round Steak

SLICED STEAK AU JUS
(180 calories per serving)

1 1¾-pound beef
  top-round steak,
  cut about 1 inch
  thick
1 2½-or 3-ounce can
  sliced mushrooms,
  drained
1 garlic clove,
  minced

1 tablespoon
  Worcestershire
1 tablespoon lemon
  juice
½ teaspoon salt
dash pepper
parsley sprigs for
  garnish

ABOUT 1¾ HOURS BEFORE SERVING:

On cutting board, trim any excess fat from steak; then cut into ¼ inch slices. In 12" by 8" baking dish arrange steak slices. Sprinkle mushrooms and remaining ingredients except parsley over steak. Cover with foil. Bake in 350°F. oven 1 hour. Remove foil; if necessary, bake about 15 minutes longer or until meat is fork-tender, basting occasionally. Garnish with parsley. Makes 6 servings.

CHICKEN BREASTS WITH CARROT & ZUCCHINI STUFFING
(180 calories per serving)

2 small whole
  chicken breasts
1 cup shredded car-
  rots (about 2
  small)
1 cup shredded
  zucchini (about 1
  medium)

1 teaspoon salt
¼ teaspoon poultry
  seasoning
1 envelope chicken-
  flavor bouillon
¼ cup water

ABOUT 1¼ HOURS BEFORE SERVING:

With sharp knife, remove skin and excess fat from chicken breasts. Cut each breast in half along breastbone; remove breastbone. From cut side of each chicken-breast half, with tip of sharp knife, cut and scrape meat away from rib cage, gently pulling back meat to form "pocket"; set aside.

In medium bowl, combine carrots, zucchini, salt and poultry seasoning. Spoon about ½ cup mixture into each "pocket"; secure with toothpicks. In 10-inch skillet, place chicken; sprinkle with bouillon. To skillet, add water. Over medium high heat, heat to boiling. Reduce heat to low; cover and simmer about 40 minutes or until chicken is fork-tender. Remove toothpicks. Makes 4 servings.

FISH FILLETS WITH CUCUMBER SAUCE
(160 calories per serving)

1 tablespoon salad
  oil
2 16-ounce packages
  frozen flounder or
  ocean perch fillets
½ teaspoon salt
¼ cup butter or
  margarine

2 medium
  cucumbers,
  scored and thinly
  sliced
1 medium onion,
  thinly slices
2 tablespoons white
  wine vinegar
¼ teaspoon pepper

ABOUT 40 MINUTES BEFORE SERVING:

Remove frozen fillets from freezer and allow to stand at room temperature for 15 minutes. Meanwhile, brush 13" by 9" baking dish with salad oil. With sharp knife, cut each package of frozen fish fillets crosswise into 4 pieces; place fillets in baking dish; sprinkle with salt. Bake in 450°F. oven 20 to 25 minutes until fish flakes easily when tested with a fork.

About 10 minutes before fish is done, in 2-quart saucepan over medium heat, in hot butter or margarine, cook cucumbers, onion, vinegar and pepper 5 minutes, stirring occasionally.

To serve, spoon sauce over and around fish. Makes 8 servings.

Fillets with Cucumber Sauce

TURKEY CUTLETS IN MUSHROOM SAUCE

(150 calories per serving)

2 tablespoons salad oil
8 turkey cutlets, each cut about ¼ inch thick (about 1½ pounds)*
1 4½-ounce jar sliced mushrooms, drained
1 cup buttermilk
1 teaspoon salt
dash pepper

ABOUT 45 MINUTES BEFORE SERVING:

In 12-inch skillet over high heat, in 1 tablespoon hot salad oil, cook turkey cutlets, a few pieces at a time, until both sides are lightly browned and tender, adding 1 tablespoon salad oil if needed. Place cutlets on platter; keep warm.

Reduce heat to low; in same skillet, heat remaining ingredients until hot, stirring constantly (do not boil); pour over cutlets. Makes 8 servings.

*Or, from one 4- to 5-pound frozen turkey breast, slightly thawed, remove and discard skin. Slice four ¼-inch-thick cutlets from one side of breast and another four ¼-inch-thick cutlets from the remaining side of breast (about 1½ pounds of meat). Use remaining turkey and carcass in hearty soup another day.

FISH FILLETS WITH HERB-LEMON TOPPING

(115 calories per serving)

ABOUT 20 MINUTES BEFORE SERVING:

Preheat broiler if manufacturer directs. In 1-quart saucepan over low heat, in melted 1 tablespoon butter or margarine, stir in 2 tablespoons lemon juice. Place fillets from one 16-ounce package frozen cod, Greenland turbot, flounder or sole fillets, thawed, in one layer on rack in broiling pan. Baste with some lemon-butter mixture; broil 5 to 8 minutes or until fish flakes easily when tested with a fork, basting with lemon-butter mixture once more during cooking. Sprinkle fillets with ¼ cup Herb-Lemon Topping. (below). Makes 4 servings.

HERB-LEMON TOPPING:

(5 calories per tablespoon)

ABOUT 15 MINUTES BEFORE SERVING:

In small bowl, mix well ½ cup chopped parsley, 1 tablespoon grated lemon peel, 2 teaspoons chopped chives, ¼ teaspoon salt and dash pepper. Sprinkle over fish, boiled potatoes, cooked carrots and broiled chicken. Cover and refrigerate. Use within 3 days. Makes about ½ cup.

STUFFED CORNISH HENS

(460 calories per serving)

¼ cup chicken bouillon
¼ cup dry white wine
¼ teaspoon thyme leaves
¼ teaspoon parsley leaves
2 4½-ounce jars sliced mushrooms, drained
1 cup finely chopped celery
1 cup fresh or frozen chopped onion
⅛ teaspoon pepper salt
4 1-pound Rock Cornish hens

ABOUT 2 HOURS BEFORE SERVING:

1. In small bowl, stir bouillon, wine, thyme and parsley; set aside.
2. In large bowl, combine mushrooms, celery, onion, pepper and ½ teaspoon salt.
3. Preheat oven to 375°F. Remove giblets and necks from hens. (Use giblets and necks in a soup another day.) Rinse hens and drain well. Tuck neck skin of hens under wings to secure them. Lightly sprinkle cavities and outside of hens with salt. Lightly spoon mushroom mixture into cavities. With string, tie legs and tail of each hen together.
4. Place hens, breast-side up, in 13" by 9" roasting pan; pour bouillon mixture over hens. Roast hens, brushing every 15 minutes with liquid in pan, for 1¼ hours or until a leg can be moved easily up and down. Remove strings. Skim fat from juice in pan and serve juice with hens. Makes 4 servings.

(Clockwise from top)

Mock Beef Stroganoff
Eggs Benedict with
    Asparagus
Zucchini "Lasagna"
Turkey Cutlets in
    Mushroom Sauce
Fish Fillets with Herb-
    Lemon Topping
Stuffed Cornish Hens

MOCK BEEF STROGANOFF
(280 calories per serving)

1 1-pound beef steak top round unseasoned meat tenderizer
2 tablespoons butter or margarine
1 10½-ounce can condensed beef bouillon
1 medium onion, thinly sliced
½ pound mushrooms, thinly sliced
½ cup buttermilk
3 tablespoons all-purpose flour
1 teaspoon salt
⅛ teaspoon pepper
1 8-ounce package fine egg noodles, cooked and drained
2 tablespoons chopped parsley for garnish

ABOUT 45 MINUTES BEFORE SERVING:

1. On cutting board, trim and discard fat from round steak. Sprinkle meat with tenderizer as label directs. Cut meat lengthwise in half; then cut each piece diagonally against the grain, into paper-thin slices.
2. In 10-inch skillet over high heat, in hot butter or margarine, cook meat, stirring quickly and frequently with slotted spoon, until meat is browned, about 2 minutes. Spoon meat into a bowl, leaving drippings in skillet.
3. To drippings in skillet, add undiluted bouillon, onion and mushrooms; heat to boiling. Reduce heat to low; cover and simmer until tender, about 10 minutes.
4. In small bowl, blend flour, salt and pepper with buttermilk until smooth. Gradually stir mixture into skillet; add meat, and cook, stirring constantly, until sauce is thickened. On warm platter, serve mixture over noodles. Garnish with parsley. Makes 7 servings.

Fluffy Hollandaise sauce is terrific on baked fish, broccoli and Brussels Sprouts, too!

EGGS BENEDICT WITH ASPARAGUS
(275 calories per serving)

ABOUT 30 MINUTES BEFORE SERVING:

1. Prepare *1 pound asparagus:* Hold base of stalk firmly and bend stalk; end will break off at spot where it becomes too tough to eat. Discard ends; trim scales if stalks are gritty.
2. Prepare Fluffy Hollandaise Sauce (below); set aside.
3. In covered 10-inch skillet over medium heat, in ½ inch boiling water, cook asparagus with ½ teaspoon *salt* 5 minutes or until tender-crisp; drain and set aside; keep warm. Preheat broiler if manufacturer directs.
4. Meanwhile, in another 10-inch skillet over high heat, heat 1½ inches water to boiling; reduce heat to low. One at a time, break *4 eggs* into saucer and slip into simmering water. Cook eggs 3 to 5 minutes until of desired firmness. When done, carefully remove eggs from water with a slotted spoon. Drain each egg (still held in spoon) over paper towels; place on warm platter.
5. Place *4 bread slices* on broiler pan with *8 Canadian-style bacon slices,* each cut about ⅛ inch thick, alongside. Broil until bread is toasted on both sides and bacon is heated through.
6. On each plate, place 2 bacon slices on a slice of toast; top bacon with about 4 asparagus stalks and a poached egg. Spoon one-fourth of sauce over egg. Makes 4 servings.

FLUFFY HOLLANDAISE SAUCE
(65 calories per serving)

In double-boiler top, with wire whisk, beat *2 egg yolks* with *2 teaspoons lemon juice,* ½ teaspoon *salt* and a *dash pepper.* Add *1 tablespoon butter* or *margarine* to mixture and cook over hot, *not boiling,* water, beating constantly, until butter is melted and mixture is slightly thickened; remove from heat.

Meanwhile, in small bowl, with mixer at high speed, beat *2 egg whites* until stiff peaks form. Carefully fold mixture into beaten whites. Serve within a few minutes as sauce loses volume quickly. Makes about 1 cup.

ZUCCHINI "LASAGNA"
(295 calories per serving)

½ pound ground
lean beef
⅓ cup fresh or
frozen chopped
onion
1 15-ounce can
tomato sauce
½ teaspoon salt
½ teaspoon oregano
leaves
¼ teaspoon basil
⅛ teaspoon pepper

4 medium zucchini
1 8-ounce container
creamed cottage
cheese (1 cup)
1 egg
2 tablespoons all-
purpose flour
¼ pound part-
skimmed-milk
mozzarella
cheese, shredded

ABOUT 1 HOUR BEFORE SERVING:

1. In 10-inch skillet over medium-high heat, cook ground beef and onion until onion is tender, about 10 minutes, stirring occasionally. Spoon off fat. Add tomato sauce, salt, oregano, basil and pepper; heat to boiling. Reduce heat to low and simmer 5 minutes to blend flavors, stirring occasionally.
2. Preheat oven to 375°F. Meanwhile, with sharp knife, slice zucchini lengthwise into ¼-inch-thick slices. In small bowl, combine cottage cheese with egg until well mixed.
3. In bottom of 12" by 8" baking dish, arrange half of zucchini in a layer and sprinkle with a tablespoon flour. Top with cottage cheese mixture and half of meat mixture. Repeat with remaining zucchini and flour; sprinkle with mozzarella cheese and then remaining meat mixture.
4. Bake 40 minutes until hot and bubbly and zucchini is fork-tender. Let stand 10 minutes for easier cutting. Makes 6 servings.

LUNCHEON LOAF
(230 calories per serving)

1 6½-7 ounce can
water-packed
tuna, drained
⅓ 8-ounce package
pasteurized
cheese spread,
minced
1 small stalk celery,
minced (¼ cup)
3 tablespoons imita-
tion mayonnaise
2 teaspoons
prepared mustard
½ teaspoon Worces-
tershire

½ 8-ounce package
imitation cream
cheese, softened
½ cup minced
watercress
¼ cup cottage
cheese
1½ teaspoons lemon
juice
1 loaf day-old,
unsliced white
bread (about 8
inches long)
cherry tomatoes,
sliced in half for
garnish

EARLY IN DAY:

1. In small bowl, mix well tuna, cheese, celery, imitation mayonnaise, mustard and Worcestershire.
2. In another small bowl, mix well imitation cream cheese, watercress, cottage cheese, and lemon juice.
3. With long serrated knife, cut all crusts from bread. Cut bread horizontally into 4 slices.
4. Evenly spread bottom bread slice with tuna mixture. Top mixture with second bread slice; spread with imitation cream cheese mixture. Top with third bread slice (use remaining bread slice for toast another day). Wrap loaf with plastic wrap; refrigerate.

TO SERVE:

Garnish loaf with cherry tomatoes. Makes 6 servings.

Cottage cheese is not only lower in calories than the traditional ricotta, but costs less, too

Luncheon Loaf

BEEF ROLL-UPS

(360 calories per serving)

Tangy Potato Salad (below)

Zucchini Chips (below)

1 pound cold thinly sliced roast beef (about 12 slices)

1 10½-ounce can asparagus spears (drained)

ABOUT 2 HOURS BEFORE SERVING OR EARLY IN DAY:

Prepare Tangy Potato Salad.
Prepare Zucchini Chips.

ABOUT 30 MINUTES BEFORE SERVING:

On short side of a roast beef slice, spoon about ¼ cup potato salad; top with 1 or 2 asparagus spears, parallel to short side. Roll up; jelly-roll fashion. Repeat with remaining roast beef, potato salad, and asparagus.

To serve, drain zucchini. Arrange zucchini and beef roll-ups on platter. Makes 6 servings.

TANGY POTATO SALAD:

In medium bowl with fork, mix well ½ cup imitation mayonnaise, 1 teaspoon prepared mustard, 1 teaspoon sugar, ½ teaspoon salt, ¼ teaspoon cracked pepper, 1 small onion, minced. With rubber spatula, gently fold in 2 16-ounce cans whole potatoes, drained and diced. Cover and refrigerate at least 1 hour to blend flavors.

ZUCCHINI CHIPS:

In medium bowl with fork, mix well ¼ cup low-calorie Italian salad dressing and 2 teaspoons chopped parsley. Add 2 medium zucchini, thinly sliced. Gently toss to mix well; cover and refrigerate at least 1 hour to blend flavors.

OLD FASHIONED BEEF STEW

(265 calories per serving)

1 tablespoon salad oil

½ cup fresh or frozen chopped onion

1 garlic clove, minced

1¼ pounds lean beef for stew, cut into chunks

1 10½-ounce can condensed beef broth

1 cup water

1½ teaspoons salt

⅛ teaspoon pepper

1 bay leaf

3 medium potatoes, cut into chunks

½ 16-ounce bag carrots, cut into chunks

½ 10-ounce package frozen peas (¾ cup)

ABOUT 3½ HOURS BEFORE SERVING:

In 4-quart Dutch oven over medium heat, in hot salad oil, cook onion and garlic until almost tender, about 3 minutes, stirring occasionally. Add beef and next 5 ingredients; heat to boiling, stirring occasionally. Reduce heat to low; cover and simmer about 2½ hours or until meat is almost tender, stirring occasionally. Add potatoes and carrots; over medium heat, heat to boiling. Reduce heat to low; cover and simmer 20 minutes. Stir in frozen peas; cover and simmer 5 to 10 minutes. Discard bay leaf. Makes 6 servings.

Beef Roll-Ups

STUFFED PEPPERS, ITALIAN STYLE
(205 calories per serving)

½ 15½-ounce jar
  spaghetti sauce
1 12-ounce container
  cottage cheese
  (1½ cups)
¼ 8-ounce package
  mozzarella cheese,
  shredded
1 tablespoon grated
  Parmesan cheese

1 egg
¼ teaspoon oregano
  leaves
4 medium green
  peppers, halved
  lengthwise then
  seeded

ABOUT 30 MINUTES BEFORE SERVING:

Into 12-inch skillet, pour spaghetti sauce. In medium bowl, stir cottage cheese, mozzarella cheese, Parmesan cheese, egg and oregano until blended; spoon mixture into pepper halves. Arrange pepper halves on sauce; over medium heat, heat to boiling. Reduce heat to low; cover and simmer 15 minutes or until peppers are tender-crisp. To serve, spoon sauce over peppers. Makes 4 servings.

CHICKEN "MANICOTTI"
(230 calories per serving)

¾ cup tomato juice
1 small garlic clove,
  minced
¼ teaspoon salt
dash pepper
Italian seasoning
2 whole large chicken breasts
  skinned, boned and halved

½ 8-ounce container
  cottage cheese
¼ 8-ounce package
  mozzarella
  cheese, shredded

ABOUT 1¼ HOURS BEFORE SERVING:

In 1-quart saucepan over medium heat, heat tomato juice, garlic, salt, pepper and ½ teaspoon Italian seasoning to boiling. Reduce heat to low and simmer mixture 10 minutes, stirring occasionally.

Meanwhile, on cutting board, with mallet or dull edge of French knife, pound chicken pieces to about ¼-inch thickness; set aside. In small bowl, combine cottage cheese and ⅛ teaspoon Italian seasoning. Spoon cheese mixture onto centers of breasts, leaving ½ inch edge all around. From a narrow end, roll each, jelly-roll fashion; secure with toothpicks. In bottom of 10″ by 6″ baking dish, spoon half of tomato juice mixture; then arrange chicken rolls seam-side down. Spoon remaining tomato juice mixture over chicken rolls; top with mozzarella. Bake in 350°F. oven 45 minutes or until chicken is tender.

To serve, remove toothpicks; spoon pan juices over chicken. Makes 4 servings.

Poached Flounder Mediterranean

POACHED FLOUNDER MEDITERRANEAN
(185 calories per serving)

1 tablespoon salad oil	2 tablespoons minced parsley
1 medium onion, chopped	2 tablespoons dry white wine
1 medium green pepper, cut into ½-inch strips	1 small bay leaf
	½ teaspoon salt
1 medium carrot, shredded	¼ teaspoon oregano leaves
1 garlic clove, minced	¼ teaspoon thyme leaves
1 16-ounce can tomatoes	dash pepper
¾ pound eggplant, cut into ½-inch cubes	1 16-ounce package frozen flounder or sole fillets

ABOUT 50 MINUTES BEFORE SERVING:

In heavy 3-quart saucepan over medium heat, in hot salad oil, cook onion, green pepper, carrot and garlic until vegetables are tender-crisp, about 5 minutes, stirring occasionally. Add tomatoes and their liquid and remaining ingredients except fish; heat to boiling. Reduce heat to low; cover and simmer 20 minutes.

Meanwhile, remove frozen fillets from freezer and allow to stand at room temperature for 15 minutes. With sharp knife, cut package of frozen fillets crosswise into 4 pieces; place onto tomato mixture. Simmer 25 minutes longer or until fish flakes easily and vegetables are tender. Serve fish with vegetable sauce. Makes 4 servings.

DEVILED ROUND STEAK
(255 calories per serving)

1 1½-pound beef top round steak, cut about 1 inch thick	2½ tablespoons prepared mustard
	¼ teaspoon Worcestershire
unseasoned meat tenderizer	parsley sprigs for garnish
3 tablespoons butter or margarine, softened	

ABOUT 45 MINUTES BEFORE SERVING:

Preheat broiler if manufacturer directs. Prepare steak with meat tenderizer as label directs; place steak on rack in broiling pan.

In small bowl with fork, mix butter, mustard and Worcestershire until well blended. With metal spatula, spread half of mixture over top of steak; broil 7 minutes. Turn steak; spread remaining butter mixture on steak; broil 7 minutes longer for rare or until desired doneness. Garnish with parsley. Makes 6 servings.

SPICY CHICKEN WITH YOGURT
(170 calories per serving)

1 cup plain yogurt
2 teaspoons all-
  purpose flour
1 teaspoon salt
¼ teaspoon ground
  ginger

1 garlic clove,
  crushed
1 2½-to 3-pound
  broiler-fryer, cut
  up

ABOUT 5 HOURS BEFORE SERVING OR DAY AHEAD:

In medium bowl, mix all ingredients except chicken. Cut skin from chicken breasts, legs and thighs; place chicken in yogurt mixture, turning to coat well. (Use skin, wings, back, neck and giblets for stock another day.) Cover and refrigerate at least 4 hours or overnight, turning occasionally.

ABOUT 30 MINUTES BEFORE SERVING

Preheat broiler if manufacturer directs. With tongs, place chicken pieces on rack in broiling pan, about 7 to 9 inches from source of heat (or at 450°F.). Broil chicken 12 to 15 minutes on each side or until fork-tender basting often with yogurt mixture. Makes 4 servings.

POACHED RAINBOW TROUT
(135 calories per serving)

4 green onions
½ cup sauterne or
  white table wine
1 large garlic clove,
  crushed
1½ teaspoon salt
dash pepper
1 teaspoon Worces-
  tershire

3 8-ounce packages
  frozen rainbow
  trout (6 small
  trout), thawed, or
  3 10-ounce fresh
  rainbow trout,
  dressed
1 large lemon, cut
  into 6 wedges

ABOUT 30 MINUTES BEFORE SERVING:

Reserve one 4-inch piece of green onion for garnish. Thinly slice remaining onions (about ¼ cup).

In 12-inch skillet over high heat, heat sliced green onions, sauterne, garlic, salt, pepper, Worcestershire and ½ cup water to boiling. Add 3 trout and heat to boiling. (If using fresh trout, cook all at once.) Reduce heat to low; cover and simmer 8 to 10 minutes until fish flakes easily when tested with fork. Carefully place fish on warm platter. Repeat with remaining fish. Pour pan liquid over fish. Garnish with reserved green onion and lemon wedges. Makes 6 servings.

POT ROAST WITH SAUERKRAUT AND CARROTS
(395 calories per serving)

1 4-pound beef bot-
  tom round roast
1 medium onion,
  sliced
1 bay leaf
1 teaspoon salt
¼ teaspoon pepper

16-ounce cans
  sauerkraut (4 cups)
2 16-ounce bags
  carrots, cut into
  3-inch pieces (10
  medium carrots)

ABOUT 3¼ HOURS BEFORE SERVING:

Preheat oven to 350°F. Trim any excess fat from bottom round roast. In covered, 8-quart Dutch oven, bake meat, onion, bay leaf, salt, pepper and 1 cup water 2½ hours.

Add sauerkraut and carrots to meat in Dutch oven. Cover and bake 40 minutes longer or until carrots and meat are tender. Place meat on warm platter and surround with vegetables. Makes 10 servings.

CONFETTI FISH SALAD
(185 calories per serving)

1 16-ounce package
  frozen cod, or
  haddock fillets
⅓ cup salad
  dressing
1 small green
pepper, chopped

2 tablespoons
  chopped pimento
1 tablespoon minced
  onion
½ teaspoon salt
⅛ teaspoon pepper

ABOUT 2 HOURS BEFORE SERVING:

In 10-inch skillet over high heat, in 1 inch boiling water, heat frozen fish fillets to boiling. Reduce heat to low; cover and simmer about 15 minutes until fish flakes when tested with fork. With slotted spatula remove fish to medium bowl; flake into small pieces.

Add remaining ingredients; toss to mix well. Cover and refrigerate about 1½ hours or until salad is well chilled. Makes 4 main-dish servings.

(Clockwise from top)
Skillet Ham and Potatoes
Confetti Fish Salad
Round Steak Diablo
Spicy Chicken with Yogurt
Poached Rainbow Trout
Pot Roast with Sauerkraut and Carrots

SKILLET HAM AND POTATOES
(255 calories per serving)

1 tablespoon salad oil
1 24-ounce bag frozen O'Brien potatoes
1 teaspoon salt
⅛ teaspoon pepper
2 tablespoons all-purpose flour
2 tablespoons prepared mustard
1½ cups skimmed milk or reliquefied non-fat dry milk
1 pound leftover cooked smoked ham, cut into ½-inch pieces

ABOUT 20 MINUTES BEFORE SERVING:

In 12-inch cook-and-serve skillet over medium-high heat, in hot salad oil, cook frozen potatoes with salt and pepper until lightly browned, about 7 minutes, stirring occasionally.

Meanwhile, in small bowl, with fork, combine flour, mustard and milk until well blended. Stir mixture and ham into potatoes; continue cooking until sauce is thickened, stirring constantly. Reduce heat to low; cover and simmer 5 minutes or until potatoes are tender, stirring occasionally. Makes 6 servings.

CHICKEN BREASTS WITH MUSHROOMS
(205 calories per serving)

3 tablespoons salad oil
3 large whole chicken breasts (about 2½ pounds, split, skinned and boned
1 garlic clove, minced
1 10½-ounce can condensed chicken broth
½ pound fresh mushrooms, sliced
½ teaspoon salt
dash pepper
1 tablespoon cornstarch
2 tablespoons water
1 tablespoon chopped parsley

ABOUT 40 MINUTES BEFORE SERVING:

In 12-inch skillet, over medium heat in hot salad oil, cook chicken and garlic until chicken is brown on both sides. Stir in chicken broth, mushrooms, salt and pepper; heat to boiling. Reduce heat to low; cover and simmer, stirring occasionally for 30 minutes or until chicken is fork-tender.

In small cup, blend cornstarch and water until smooth; gradually stir into hot liquid in skillet and cook until thickened. Serve garnished with parsley. Makes 6 servings.

ROUND STEAK DIABLO
(260 calories per serving)

1 2-pound beef round bottom round steak, cut about 1 inch thick
1 6-ounce can tomato paste
⅓ cup fresh or frozen chopped onion
1 tablespoon dry white wine
1½ tablespoons salt
½ teaspoon sugar
dash cayenne pepper
2 cups mezzani, ziti, or small shell macaroni, cooked and drained

ABOUT 2½ HOURS BEFORE SERVING:

Trim and discard any excess fat from round steak. In 12-inch skillet over medium-high heat, stir remaining ingredients except mezzani with 2 cups water. Add meat, turning to coat with mixture; heat to boiling. Reduce heat to low; cover and simmer 1½ hours or until meat is fork-tender, turning once.

Place meat on warm platter and surround with cooked mezzani. Serve sauce over mezzani. Makes 8 servings.

Chicken Breasts with Mushrooms

a 4-ounce can
of mushrooms
drained car
substitute for
fresh mushrooms

MEATBALLS IN TOMATO-BURGUNDY SAUCE
(315 calories per serving)

1 pound extra-lean
  ground beef
1 cup fresh bread
  crumbs
1 egg
¼ cup ice water
minced parsley
1 teaspoon salt
⅛ teaspoon pepper

1 tablespoon salad
  oil
2 cups tomato juice
½ cup red Burgundy
2 garlic cloves,
  minced
1 teaspoon paprika
3 cups hot cooked
  rice

ABOUT 1 HOUR BEFORE SERVING:

In medium bowl, mix well ground beef,
bread crumbs, egg, ice water, 1 tablespoon
parsley, salt and pepper; shape mixture into
1-inch meatballs.

In 12-inch skillet over medium-high heat,
in hot salad oil, cook meatballs, a few at a
time, until browned on all sides, removing
them as they brown. Spoon off fat. In same
skillet, combine tomato juice, Burgundy,
garlic, paprika, and 2 tablespoons parsley.
Return meatballs to skillet. Over medium
heat, heat to boiling. Reduce heat to low;
cover and simmer 15 minutes or until meatballs are tender, stirring occasionally. Serve
over rice. Makes 5 servings.

CODFISH STEW
(225 calories per serving)

1 16-ounce package
  frozen cod fillets
3 bacon slices
1 medium onion
1 16-ounce can
  whole white
  potatoes
1 16-ounce can tomatoes

¼ cup catchup
1 teaspoon Worces-
  tershire
¼ teaspoon seasoned
  pepper
⅛ teaspoon thyme
  leaves

ABOUT 55 MINUTES BEFORE SERVING:

Remove frozen fillets from freezer and
allow to stand at room temperature for 15
minutes. Meanwhile, cut bacon into 1-inch
pieces; thinly slice onion; drain potatoes and
cut each potato in half. With sharp knife, cut
fillets into bite-size chunks.

In 2-quart saucepan over medium heat,
cook bacon until just limp; add onion and
cook until onion is browned. Stir in tomatoes
with their liquid, potatoes, catchup,
Worcestershire, pepper and thyme; cook 5
minutes, stirring occasionally. Add fish;
cook about 10 minutes longer or until fish
flakes easily when tested with a fork, stirring
often. Makes 4 servings.

Codfish Stew

Freezing left-over portions of the meatballs makes convenient single-serving main-dishes

25

CHINESE CHICKEN ROLLS
(150 calories per serving)

¼ small head cabbage, (1 cup)
1 green onion, minced
1 small stalk celery, thinly sliced, (¼ cup)
1 teaspoon soy sauce
⅛ teaspoon ground ginger
2 whole large chicken breasts, skinned and boned
salt
pepper
1 envelope chicken-flavor bouillon
½ cup water

ABOUT 1¼ HOURS BEFORE SERVING:

In small bowl, mix well cabbage, green onion, celery, soy sauce and ginger; set aside.

On cutting board, cut each chicken breast lengthwise in half. With mallet or dull edge of French knife, between 2 sheets of waxed paper, pound chicken pieces to about ¼ inch thickness. Sprinkle lightly with salt and pepper on one side of each piece. Top each piece with ¼ of cabbage mixture. From a narrow end, roll each, jelly-roll fashion; fasten with toothpicks.

Arrange chicken rolls in 10" by 6" baking dish; sprinkle with chicken bouillon; pour water over chicken; cover dish with foil. Bake in 350°F. oven 30 minutes. Remove foil; continue baking 15 minutes longer until chicken is tender, basting occasionally with pan juices. To serve, discard toothpicks; spoon juices over chicken. Makes 4 servings.

HAM AND FRESH-VEGETABLE MEDLEY
(305 calories per serving)

1 ¾-pound fully cooked boneless ham slice
2 large tomatoes
1 small green pepper
1 small red pepper
1 medium onion
1 medium yellow straightneck squash
2 medium zucchini (about 1 pound)
3 tablespoons salad oil
½ cup water
1 envelope chicken-flavor bouillon
2 teaspoons basil
½ teaspoon salt
¼ teaspoon pepper

With sharp knife, cut boneless ham into ¼-inch thick strips, about 3 inches long; cut each tomato into 8 wedges; cut green and red peppers into ½-inch-wide strips; cut onion, yellow squash and zucchini into ¼-inch-wide slices.

In 12-inch skillet over high heat, in hot salad oil, cook green and red peppers, onion, yellow squash, zucchini and ham, about 5 minutes, stirring frequently. Reduce heat to medium; add water, chicken-flavor bouillon, basil, salt and pepper. Cook until vegetables are tender-crisp, stirring occasionally about 5 minutes. Add tomato wedges; continue cooking until tomatoes are heated through. Makes 4 main-dish servings.

EASY BAKED PORK CHOPS
(180 calories per serving)

ABOUT 1½ HOURS BEFORE SERVING:

With sharp knife, trim fat from 6 pork loin rib chops, each cut about ¾ inch thick (about 2 pounds). In 12" by 8" baking dish, arrange pork chops in one layer. Add ¼ cup water; sprinkle 2 envelopes chicken bouillon over pork chops. Bake in 325°F. oven about 1 hour and 15 minutes or until pork chops are fork-tender, basting occasionally with pan juices during the last half hour. To serve: Spoon pan juices over pork chops. Makes 6 servings.

GROUND BEEF MARSALA
(280 calories per serving)

1 pound extra-lean ground beef
salt and pepper
½ cup sliced onion
½ pound mushrooms, sliced
½ cup dry Marsala

ABOUT 30 MINUTES BEFORE SERVING:

On waxed paper, shape ground beef into 8 flat, oval patties; sprinkle lightly with salt and pepper. In 12-inch skillet over medium heat, cook patties and onion until patties are browned on both sides, about 5 minutes. Add mushrooms, Marsala and ¼ teaspoon salt; reduce heat to low and cook 10 minutes, stirring occasionally, and turning patties once. To serve, pour sauce over patties. Makes 4 servings.

Ham and Vegetable Medley

VEGETABLES

STIR-FRIED VEGETABLE MIX
(90 calories per serving)

2 medium carrots
1 medium onion
1 small bunch
  broccoli
3 tablespoons salad oil
¾ teaspoon salt
½ teaspoon sugar
1 4-ounce can whole
  mushrooms

ABOUT 30 MINUTES BEFORE SERVING:

Cut carrots into matchstick-thin strips. Thinly slice onion. Cut broccoli into 2" by ½" pieces.

In 12-inch skillet over high heat, in hot salad oil, cook carrots, onion and broccoli, stirring quickly and frequently, about 3 to 4 minutes. Add salt, sugar and mushrooms with their liquid; cover and cook 5 to 6 minutes longer until vegetables are tender-crisp, stirring occasionally. Makes 6 servings.

CAULIFLOWER PARMESAN
(65 calories per serving)

1 medium fresh
  cauliflower
½ teaspoon salt
4 teaspoons olive oil
1 garlic clove,
  minced
1 tablespoon
  chopped parsley
¼ cup grated
  Parmesan cheese

ABOUT 30 MINUTES BEFORE SERVING:

Wash cauliflower; divide into flowerets. In medium saucepan over medium-high heat, in 1 inch boiling water, heat cauliflower and salt to boiling; cover and cook 10 to 15 minutes until fork-tender; drain well.

In medium skillet, over medium heat, in hot oil, saute garlic and parsley 2 minutes; add cauliflower and saute 2 minutes more. Remove from heat; sprinkle with cheese. Makes 6 servings of about ½ cup each.

CARAWAY RED CABBAGE
(55 calories per serving)

2 tablespoons butter
  or margarine
1 medium onion,
  chopped
4 teaspoons
  granulated sugar
2½ teaspoons salt
1½ teaspoons
  caraway seed
4 teaspoons white
  vinegar
1 large red cabbage
  (about 3 pounds),
  shredded

ABOUT 1 HOUR BEFORE SERVING:

In large saucepan, over medium heat, in hot butter, saute onions until golden; stir in sugar. Add 1 cup water and remaining ingredients. Over high heat, heat to boiling. Reduce heat to low; cover and simmer, stirring occasionally, about 35 minutes, or until cabbage is tender. Makes 12 servings.

ASPARAGUS AUX HERBES
(40 calories per serving)

1 10-ounce package
  frozen asparagus
  spears
¼ cup water
2 tablespoons chopped chives
1½ teaspoons butter
  or margarine
¼ teaspoon salt

ABOUT 20 MINUTES BEFORE SERVING:

Run warm water over asparagus, just enough to separate spears. Meanwhile, in medium skillet, over medium heat, heat water, chives, butter or margarine and salt to boiling. Immediately add asparagus. Reduce heat to low, cover and simmer 15 minutes or until tender-crisp. Makes 3 servings.

MARINATED VEGETABLES
(120 calories per serving)

1 small head cauli-
 flower, separated
 into flowerets
6 medium carrots,
 sliced
1 16-ounce can
 whole green
 beans, drained
1 6- to 7¾-ounce
 can extra large
 pitted ripe olives,
 drained

1 red onion, sliced in
 rings
½ pound
 mushrooms, sliced
1 pint cherry
 tomatoes
1 green pepper, cut
 into strips
6 8-ounce bottles
 (6 cups) low-
 calorie Italian
 dressing

EARLY IN DAY OR DAY AHEAD:

In 4-quart tall glass container, place
cauliflower; layer next 7 ingredients on top.
Carefully pour dressing over vegetables;
cover; refrigerate at least 8 hours. Makes 14
accompaniment servings.

ITALIAN-STYLE TOMATOES
(40 calories per serving)

2 16-ounce cans
 Italian plum
 tomatoes
1 small onion,
 minced
2 tablespoons
 granulated sugar

1 tablespoon basil
1 teaspoon salt
1 teaspoon Worces-
 tershire
⅛ teaspoon pepper

ABOUT 15 MINUTES BEFORE SERVING:

In saucepan, combine all ingredients; simmer 5 minutes. Makes 8 servings of ½-cup
each.

Marinated Vegetables

Italian-style tomatoes are great with meatloaf.

PARSLEY CREAMED PARSNIPS
(50 calories per serving)

1 pound parsnips
salt
2 tablespoons all-
purpose flour
½ cup skimmed milk
or reliquefied non-fat dry milk
⅛ teaspoon pepper
1 teaspoon grated
orange peel
chopped parsley

ABOUT 30 MINUTES BEFORE SERVING:

Peel parsnips, then slice into ⅛-inch slices. In 2-quart saucepan over high heat, heat parsnips, 1 cup water and ½ teaspoon salt to boiling. Reduce heat to medium; cover and cook until parsnips are fork-tender, about 10 minutes.

Drain parsnips, reserving ½ cup liquid. In 1-quart saucepan over medium heat, stir flour with skimmed milk until well mixed. Add reserved liquid, pepper and ½ tea-spoon salt; cook, stirring constantly, until thickened and smooth. Stir in grated orange peel. Stir sauce with parsnips. Sprinkle with chopped parsley. Makes 6 servings.

ARTICHOKES WITH ORANGE SAUCE
(65 calories per serving)

ABOUT 1 HOUR BEFORE SERVING:

With sharp knife, cut stems from *4 medium artichokes* and 1 inch of leaves straight across top. With scissors, trim thorny tips from leaves. Remove loose leaves around the bottom. Gently spread leaves apart and rinse under running cold water.

In 5-quart Dutch oven, in 1 inch water, place artichokes, stem ends down; over high heat, heat to boiling. Reduce heat to low; cover and simmer 30 minutes or until centers are fork-tender.

Prepare *Orange Sauce* (below). Serve artichokes with sauce. Makes 4 servings.

ORANGE SAUCE
(20 calories per serving)

In 1-quart saucepan, mix *1 tablespoon cornstarch and ½ teaspoon salt* with *½ cup chicken broth* and *⅓ cup orange juice* until well blended. Over medium heat, cook, stirring constantly until mixture is boiling and slightly thickened. Serve warm.

BRAISED CELERY A L'ORANGE
(55 calories per serving)

1 large bunch celery
or about 12 stalks
1 teaspoon powdered
chicken stock
1 teaspoon salt
2 medium oranges,
peeled and sliced
1 tablespoon toasted
sesame seed

ABOUT 30 MINUTES BEFORE SERVING:

Remove outer row of celery ribs; trim root ends. Cut celery stalks crosswise in half. In 10-inch skillet over high heat, heat 1 cup water, celery, powdered chicken stock and salt to boiling. Reduce heat to low; cover and simmer 10 to 12 minutes or until tender-crisp, turning occasionally.

Add orange slices; cover and continue simmering 5 minutes longer or until heated through. Arrange celery and oranges with their liquid in warm vegetable dish. Sprinkle with toasted sesame seed. Makes 4 servings.

HOT CABBAGE SLAW
(35 calories per serving)

3 tablespoons cider
vinegar
1 teaspoon sugar
1 teaspoon salt
¼ teaspoon tarragon
leaves
1 small head cab-
bage, shredded
(8 cups)
1 large red cooking
apple, cut into
bite-size pieces

ABOUT 30 MINUTES BEFORE SERVING:

In covered 12-inch skillet over medium heat, cook first 5 ingredients 15 minutes or until cabbage is tender-crisp, stirring often. Remove from heat; stir in apple. Makes 6 servings.

Low-Calorie Toppings for potatoes make delicious "skinny" party dips

(Clockwise from top)
Parsley Creamed Parsnips
Hot Cabbage Slaw
Low-Calorie Toppings
Artichokes with Orange Slaw
Braised Celery A L'Orange

BROCCOLI WITH MUSTARD SAUCE
(60 calories per serving)

2 10-ounce packages
  frozen broccoli
  spears
1 tablespoon butter
  or margarine
1 tablespoon all-
  purpose flour

1 tablespoon pre-
  pared mustard
1 cup skimmed milk
  or reliquefied non-
  fat dry milk
1½ teaspoon lemon
  juice

ABOUT 15 MINUTES BEFORE SERVING:

Cook broccoli as label directs; drain.
Meanwhile, in small saucepan over medium
heat, melt butter or margarine; stir in flour
and mustard until blended. Slowly add milk;
cook, stirring constantly, until smooth and
thickened. Remove from heat; stir in lemon
juice. Serve on broccoli. Makes 6 servings.

CREAMED CELERY
(45 calories per serving)

1 tablespoon butter
  or margarine
4 stalks green celery,
  diced (2 cups)
2 tablespoons finely
  minced onion
½ teaspoon salt

1 teaspoon corn-
  starch
¼ cup skimmed milk
  or reliquefied
  non-fat dry milk
generous dash
  pepper

ABOUT 25 MINUTES BEFORE SERVING:

In skillet over low heat, in hot butter or
margarine, saute celery and onion until
onion is golden. Add ¼ cup water and salt.
Reduce heat to low; cover; and simmer
gently 10 minutes, or until celery is tender-
crisp.

Meanwhile, combine cornstarch, milk and
pepper. Stirring constantly, add to cooked
celery; heat until thickened and smooth.
Makes four ½-cup servings.

JULIAN'S CARROTS
(60 calories per serving)

10 medium carrots,
  thickly sliced
1 15¼-ounce can
  pineapple chunks
  packed in own
  juice

1 cup orange juice
1 tablespoon corn-
  starch
1 teaspoon salt
½ teaspoon
  cinnamon

ABOUT 20 MINUTES BEFORE SERVING:

In medium saucepan, over medium-high
heat, in 1 inch boiling water, heat carrots to
boiling. Reduce heat to low, cover and simmer 15 minutes or until tender, drain.

Into small saucepan, drain juice from
pineapple and add orange juice. In small
bowl, mix cornstarch, salt and cinnamon; stir
in a few tablespoons juice; mix to smooth
paste.

Over medium heat, heat juices, stir in
cornstarch mixture. Reduce heat to low, simmer, stirring constantly, until thickened.
Add pineapple chunks and carrots; cook
over low heat, stirring constantly, until hot
and bubbly. Makes 10 servings.

VEGETABLE GRAVY
(20 calories per serving)

1 8-ounce can sliced
  carrots
1 tablespoon salad
  oil
1 medium onion,
  thinly sliced

1 cup water
3 beef-flavor
  boullion
  envelopes
¾ teaspoon bottled
  sauce for gravy

ABOUT 30 MINUTES BEFORE SERVING:

Drain carrots; reserving liquid. Set carrots
and liquid aside. In 2-quart saucepan over
medium heat, in hot salad oil, cook onion until tender, about 10 minutes, stirring occasionally. Add reserved liquid, water,
bouillon and bottled sauce for gravy; heat to
boiling. Reduce heat to low; cover and simmer 5 minutes. Add reserved carrots; heat
through. In covered blender container at
high speed, ladle in hot liquid and
vegetables; blend until smooth. Makes about
2 cups (eight ¼-cup gravy servings).

The crunchiness in the creamed celery adds pizazz to plain meat dinners

SOUTHERN SPINACH
(40 calories per serving)

1 10-ounce package
   frozen chopped
   spinach
1 8-ounce can
   grapefruit sections
1 teaspoon lemon
   juice
½ teaspoon salt
cinnamon
pepper

ABOUT 20 MINUTES BEFORE SERVING:

Cook spinach according to package directions, but substitute juice drained from grapefruit for water. During last minutes of cooking time, add grapefruit sections to heat through. Drain and toss with lemon juice and salt. Serve in warm bowl; sprinkle lightly with cinnamon and pepper. Makes 6 servings.

LEMON MINT BEANS
(25 calories per serving)

1 9-ounce package
   frozen cut green
   beans
1 9-ounce package
   frozen cut wax
   beans
2 tablespoons lemon juice
1 teaspoon dried
   mint leaves
½ teaspoon grated
   lemon peel
½ teaspoon salt

ABOUT 15 MINUTES BEFORE SERVING:

In medium saucepan, cook green beans and wax beans together as labels direct, but use 1 cup water; drain. Add remaining ingredients and toss well. Makes 6 servings.

Low-Calorie Vegetable Toppings

DILL CREAM
(30 calories per 2 tablespoon serving)

ABOUT 10 MINUTES BEFORE SERVING:

In covered blender container at medium-high speed, blend one 8-ounce container creamed cottage (1 cup), 1 teaspoon dill weed, ¼ teaspoon salt and ⅛ teaspoon pepper until smooth and creamy, adding up to 1 tablespoon water, if necessary. Serve over vegetables. Makes about 1 cup.

PICKLE RELISH CREAM:
(35 calories per 2 tablespoon serving)

ABOUT 10 MINUTES BEFORE SERVING:

In covered blender container at medium-high speed, blend one 8-ounce container creamed cottage cheese (1 cup), 2 tablespoons sweet pickle relish, ¼ teaspoon salt and ⅛ teaspoon pepper until smooth and creamy, adding up to 1 tablespoon water, if necessary. Serve over vegetables. Makes about 1 cup.

ONION CREAM
(35 calories per 2 tablespoon serving)

ABOUT 10 MINUTES BEFORE SERVING:

In covered blender container at medium-high speed, blend one 8-ounce container creamed cottage cheese (1 cup), 1 small white onion, halved, ⅛ teaspoon salt and ⅛ teaspoon pepper until smooth and creamy, adding up to 1 tablespoon water, if necessary. Serve over vegetables. Makes about 1 cup.

WORCESTERSHIRE CREAM:
(35 calories per 2 tablespoon serving)

ABOUT 10 MINUTES BEFORE SERVING:

In covered blender container at medium-high speed, blend one 8-ounce container creamed cottage cheese (1 cup), 1 tablespoon Worcestershire, ⅛ teaspoon salt and ⅛ teaspoon pepper until smooth and creamy, adding up to 1 tablespoon water, if necessary. Serve over vegetables. Makes about 1 cup.

SOUPS

These soups
start a dinner
with a flair;
add heartiness
to a sandwich
lunch, too.

ZESTY TOMATO-CABBAGE SOUP
(65 calories per serving)

1 46-ounce can
   tomato juice
2 beef-flavor
   bouillon cubes or
   envelopes
1 medium head
   cabbage, coarsely
   shredded
1 cup water

1 medium onion,
   sliced
1 garlic clove,
   minced
1 tablespoon salt
1 tablespoon sugar
1 tablespoon lemon
   juice
¼ teaspoon hot
   pepper sauce

ABOUT 45 MINUTES BEFORE SERVING:

In 4-quart saucepan, combine all ingredients. Over medium-high heat, heat to boiling. Reduce heat to low; cover and simmer
30 minutes or until cabbage is tender. Makes
about 10 cups or 10 first-course servings.

Zesty Tomato Cabbage Soup

ONION SOUP
(105 calories per serving)

2 tablespoons butter
 or margarine
5 cups sliced onions
4 cups hot water

4 onion-flavor
 bouillon cubes or
 envelopes
1 tablespoon
 Worcestershire

ABOUT 45 MINUTES BEFORE SERVING:

In 3-quart heavy saucepan over low heat, in hot butter or margarine, cook onions 30 minutes, stirring occasionally. Add hot water, bouillon and Worcestershire. Increase heat to high; heat to boiling. Reduce heat to low; cover and simmer about 5 minutes or until onions are tender. Makes about 5½ cups or 5 first-course servings.

OLD-FASHIONED BEET SOUP
(70 calories per serving)

2 pounds beef shank
 soup bones
5 cups hot water
½ cup fresh or
 frozen chopped
 onion
3½ teaspoons salt
¼ teaspoon pepper

1½ pounds beets,
 peeled and
 shredded
1 tablespoon sugar
1 tablespoon lemon
 juice
1 teaspoon grated
 lemon peel

ABOUT 1 HOUR BEFORE SERVING:

In 4-quart saucepan over high heat, heat bones, hot water, onion, salt and pepper to boiling. Reduce heat to low; cover and simmer 30 minutes. Add shredded beets, sugar, lemon juice and lemon peel. Increase heat to high; heat to boiling. Reduce heat to low and simmer about 20 minutes or until beets are tender. Discard bones. Skim any fat from surface of soup. Makes about 6½ cups or 6 first-course servings.

BEEF BROTH WITH HAM, BAMBOO SHOOTS & PEAS
(90 calories per serving)

2 10½-ounce cans
 condensed beef
 broth
2 soup-cans water
1 8-ounce can
 bamboo shoots,
 rinsed and drained

1 cup frozen peas
¼ pound sliced
 cooked ham, cut
 into thin strips
1 teaspoon soy sauce
⅛ teaspoon ground
 ginger

ABOUT 20 MINUTES BEFORE SERVING:

In 3-quart saucepan over medium-high heat, heat all ingredients to boiling. Reduce heat to low and cook about 5 minutes or until peas are tender. Makes about 6½ cups or 6 first-course servings.

CREAM OF TURNIP SOUP
(80 calories per serving)

1 10¾-ounce can
 condensed
 chicken broth
1 pound turnips,
 peeled and diced
1 medium carrot,
 thinly sliced
¼ cup fresh or frozen
 chopped onion

1 bay leaf
1 teaspoon salt
¼ teaspoon paprika
⅛ teaspoon pepper
2 cups skimmed or
 reliquefied non-fat
 dry milk

ABOUT 30 MINUTES BEFORE SERVING:

In 3-quart saucepan over medium-high heat, heat undiluted broth and remaining ingredients except milk to boiling. Reduce heat to low; cover and simmer 20 minutes or until vegetables are tender. Stir in milk; heat through. Discard bay leaf. Makes about 5 cups or 5 first-course servings.

HERBED VEGETABLE SOUP
(75 calories per serving)

4 cups water
5 vegetable-flavor
  bouillon cubes or
  envelopes
1 10-ounce package
frozen mixed vegetables

1 small potato, diced
1 stalk celery, sliced
  (about ½ cup)
¼ teaspoon thyme
  leaves

ABOUT 25 MINUTES BEFORE SERVING:

In 3-quart saucepan over medium-high heat, heat all ingredients to boiling. Reduce heat to low; cover and simmer 15 minutes or until vegetables are tender. Makes about 5⅓ cups or 5 first-course servings.

MINI-MEATBALLS AND SPINACH SOUP
(75 calories per serving)

¼ pound extra-lean
  ground beef
2 teaspoons dried
  bread crumbs
¼ teaspoon salt
dash pepper
5 chicken-flavor bouillon
  cubes or envelopes

4 cups water
2 cups lightly
  packed
  fresh spinach,
  coarsely shredded

ABOUT 30 MINUTES BEFORE SERVING:

In medium bowl, combine meat, bread crumbs, salt and pepper. On waxed paper, by rounded ¼ teaspoonfuls, form meat mixture into about 40 meatballs; set aside. In 3-quart saucepan over medium heat, heat bouillon and water to boiling. Add meatballs and cook about 5 minutes; then add spinach and continue cooking about 3 minutes longer. Makes about 4½ cups or 4 first-course servings.

CREAM OF GREEN-BEAN SOUP
(75 calories per serving)

1 16-ounce can cut
  green beans
1 10¾-ounce can
  condensed cream
  of celery soup

½ cup water
½ teaspoon chili
  powder
¼ teaspoon salt
bread crumbs

ABOUT 15 MINUTES BEFORE SERVING:

In covered blender container at high speed, blend green beans and their liquid until smooth. In 2-quart saucepan, combine pureed green beans with undiluted soup, water, chili powder and salt. Over medium-high heat, heat to boiling, stirring occasionally. Makes about 3½ cups or 4 first-course servings. Garnish with bread crumbs.

Low-calorie soups make filling in-between meal snacks

Cream of Green Bean Soup

SALADS & DRESSINGS

TUNA CHEF'S SALAD
(275 calories per serving)

1 medium head ice-
  berg lettuce
1 3¼- or 3½-ounce
  can tuna, drained
  and separated into
  chucks
½ 8-ounce package
  Swiss cheese
  slices, cut into thin
  strips

½ 6-ounce package
  cooked ham slices,
  cut into thin strips
2 medium tomatoes,
  cut into wedges
2 hard-cooked eggs,
  quartered
Zesty Low-Calorie
  Dressing (below)

ABOUT 45 MINUTES BEFORE SERVING:

Into large bowl, tear lettuce into bite size
pieces. On lettuce, arrange tuna, Swiss
cheese, ham, tomato and egg wedges in
separate piles. Serve with Zesty Low-Calorie
Dressing. Makes 4 main-dish servings.

ZESTY LOW-CALORIE DRESSING
(5 calories per tablespoon)

In covered blender container at medium
speed, blend ½ cup tomato juice, ⅓ cup
fresh or frozen chopped onion, 3 tablespoons
red wine vinegar, ⅛ teaspoon garlic powder,
1 teaspoon sugar, ½ teaspoon salt and ¼
teaspoon oregano until smooth and slightly
thickened. Stir before serving. Makes 1 cup.

LEMON'D BEET SALAD
(60 calories per serving)

2 teaspoons grated
  lemon peel
1 16-ounce can
  sliced beets,
  drained
¼ cup fresh chopped onion

1 tablespoon imita-
  tion mayonnaise
¾ teaspoon salt
dash pepper

**ABOUT 3 HOURS BEFORE SERVING OR
DAY AHEAD:**

In medium bowl, toss 1 teaspoon grated
lemon peel with remaining ingredients until
well combined; refrigerate at least 2½ hours
to blend flavors. Garnish salad with remaining 1 teaspoon lemon peel before serving.
Makes 4 servings.

EGG SALAD ON LETTUCE "HERO"
(100 calories per serving)

3 hard-cooked eggs
1 stalk celery,
  minced (about ¼
  cup)
1 medium dill pickle,
  minced (¼ cup)
2 tablespoons Mock
  Mayonnaise
  (below)

dash pepper
1 medium tomato
  thinly sliced
3 Romaine lettuce
  leaves
salt

ABOUT 30 MINUTES BEFORE SERVING:

In medium bowl with fork, mash eggs. Add
celery, pickle, Mock Mayonnaise and pepper; mix well. Lengthwise on half of each lettuce leaf, spread egg mixture; top with
tomato; sprinkle with salt. To serve,
lengthwise fold lettuce leaf over egg mixture;
hold as sandwich. Makes 3 servings.

MOCK MAYONNAISE
(30 calories per tablespoon)

1 cup cottage cheese
2 tablespoons salad
  oil
1 tablespoon cider
  vinegar
2 teaspoons sugar

½ teaspoon salt
½ teaspoon dry
  mustard
½ teaspoon paprika
dash pepper

**ABOUT 5 MINUTES BEFORE SERVING OR
UP TO 2 WEEKS AHEAD:**

In covered blender container at medium
speed, blend all ingredients until smooth,
stopping occasionally to scrape container
with rubber spatula. Cover and refrigerate.
Use within 2 weeks. Makes 1 cup.

*What a great
mayonnaise
substitute for
fish and meat
salads*

GAZPACHO-CHEESE SALAD
(140 calories per serving)

2 green onions,
  chopped
1 medium firm
  tomato, diced
1 16-ounce container
  cottage cheese
1 small cucumber,
  diced (½ cup)

1 small green
  pepper, diced
⅛ teaspoon salt
⅛ teaspoon hot
  pepper sauce
lettuce leaves

ABOUT 30 MINUTES BEFORE SERVING:

In medium bowl, toss all ingredients except lettuce. Serve on lettuce-lined plates. Makes 4 main-dish servings.

TANGY CHEESE DRESSING
(15 calories per tablespoon)

1 8-ounce container
  creamed cottage
  cheese
⅓ cup evaporated
  skimmed milk
2 tablespoons water
1 teaspoon vinegar

½ teaspoon garlic
  salt
½ teaspoon onion
  salt
¼ teaspoon salt
dash hot pepper
  sauce

ABOUT 1 HOUR BEFORE SERVING:

In covered blender container, at low speed, blend all ingredients until smooth—2 to 3 minutes. Chill until serving time. Delicious over salad greens. Makes 1¼ cups.

CALIFORNIA CUCUMBER SALAD
(65 calories per serving)

2 medium
  cucumbers,
  shredded and well
  drained
⅓ cup dark seedless
  raisins
¼ cup chopped
  California walnuts

¼ cup plain
  yogurt
1 teaspoon sugar
1 teaspoon salt
lettuce leaves

ABOUT 20 MINUTES BEFORE SERVING:

In medium bowl, toss all ingredients except lettuce. Serve on lettuce-lined salad plates. Makes 4 servings.

ISLAND FRUIT DRESSING
(20 calories per tablespoon)

1 cup crushed pine-
  apple, drained
1 tablespoon butter
  or margarine

1½ teaspoons curry
dash salt
1 teaspoon corn-
  starch

AT LEAST 3 HOURS BEFORE SERVING:

In small saucepan, over medium-high heat, heat pineapple, butter or margarine, curry and salt to boiling. Blend cornstarch with ⅓ cup water; stir into pineapple mixture and cook, stirring constantly, until thickened and boiling. Refrigerate; serve as dressing for crab or tuna salad. Makes 1 cup.

HORSERADISH-HERB DRESSING
(10 calories per tablespoon)

1 8-ounce container
  plain yogurt
½ to 1 tablespoon
  white prepared
  horseradish
1 tablespoon tar-
  ragon or garlic
  vinegar

1 tablespoon chop-
  ped chives
1 tablespoon fresh
  chopped dill
1 tablespoon granu-
  lated sugar
¾ teaspoon salt
¼ teaspoon paprika

AT LEAST 4 HOURS BEFORE SERVING:

In medium bowl, stir together all ingredients. Cover; refrigerate until serving time. Use within 3 days. Makes about 1 cup.

DELICATE SALAD DRESSING
(5 calories per tablespoon)

1 tablespoon
  granulated sugar
1½ teaspoon corn-
  starch
½ teaspoon salt
½ teaspoon dry
  mustard

⅓ cup vinegar
⅓ cup water
⅓ cup tomato juice
1 tablespoon minced
  onion

AT LEAST 1 HOUR BEFORE SERVING:

In medium saucepan, mix sugar, cornstarch, salt and mustard; stir in rest of ingredients. Over medium heat, heat mixture just to boiling. Pour into jar; cover; refrigerate. Seasonings may be adjusted to taste, if desired. Makes 1 cup.

YOGURT DRESSING
(20 calories per tablespoon)

1 8-ounce container
plain yogurt
2 tablespoons salad
oil
1 tablespoon lemon
juice

1 teaspoon paprika
1 teaspoon salt
¼ teaspoon garlic
powder
dash hot pepper
sauce

AT LEAST 1 HOUR BEFORE SERVING:

In jar, with tight-fitting lid combine all ingredients; shake until well blended. Refrigerate. Makes 1 cup.

WATERCRESS-ROQUEFORT DRESSING
(15 calories per tablespoon)

2 tablespoons soft
Roquefort cheese
⅓ cup imitation
mayonnaise

¼ cup skimmed milk
or reliquified non-
fat dry milk
2 tablespoons chop-
ped watercress

AT LEAST 2 HOURS BEFORE SERVING:

In small bowl, mash Roquefort, and blend with remaining ingredients until creamy. Refrigerate. Makes ⅔ cup.

PIQUANT SALAD DRESSING
(10 calories per tablespoon)

1 cup tomato juice
1 tablespoon corn-
starch
2 tablespoons salad
oil
¼ cup vinegar
1 teaspoon salt
½ teaspoon Worces-
tershire
¼ teaspoon
prepared horse-
radish

¼ teaspoon paprika
¼ teaspoon onion
salt
¼ teaspoon celery
salt
scant ⅛ teaspoon dry
mustard
2 dashes garlic salt

AT LEAST 2 HOURS BEFORE SERVING:

In small saucepan, heat ½ cup water, tomato juice and cornstarch, stirring constantly, until thickened. Cool to lukewarm; add remaining ingredients and beat until blended. Refrigerate. Shake well before serving. Makes 1¾ cups.

CREAMY FRENCH DRESSING
(15 calories per tablespoon)

2 tablespoons corn-
starch
1 tablespoon salt
4½ teaspoons
paprika
½ teaspoon dry
mustard

¼ teaspoon pepper
1 garlic clove,
crushed
½ cup red wine
vinegar
¼ cup salad
oil

ABOUT 2½ HOURS BEFORE SERVING:

In 1-quart saucepan, stir all ingredients with 2 cups water until well mixed. Over medium heat, cook, stirring frequently, until mixture is boiling and slightly thickened. Cover and refrigerate dressing to chill; serve within 1 week. Shake dressing well before using. Makes about 2½ cups.

OLD-FASHIONED FRENCH DRESSING
(10 calories per tablespoon)

⅔ cup creamed
cottage cheese
½ cup tomato juice

1 envelope (.6
ounces) French
salad-dressing mix

AT LEAST 1 HOUR BEFORE SERVING:

In covered blender container, at medium speed, blend all ingredients until smooth; refrigerate until serving time. Makes 1 cup

TORINO DRESSING
(3 calories per tablespoon)

⅓ cup tomato juice
¼ cup vinegar
2 tablespoons water

1 envelope (.6
ounces) Italian
salad-dressing mix

AT LEAST 1 HOUR BEFORE SERVING:

Combine all ingredients in small bowl; refrigerate until serving time. Makes ⅔ cup.

DESSERTS

FRESH FRUIT WITH CREAMY DRESSING
(125 calories per serving)

1 large orange,
  peeled and cut
  into bite-size
  pieces
1 banana, cut into
  chunks

1 large red eating
  apple, cored
  thinly sliced
Creamy Dressing
  (below)

ABOUT 20 MINUTES BEFORE SERVING:

In medium bowl, toss fruit. Serve with Creamy Dressing. Makes 4 servings.

CREAMY DRESSING: In covered blender container at high speed, blend ½ cup cottage cheese, ¼ cup orange juice, 1½ teaspoons lemon juice, 1 teaspoon honey and ⅛ teaspoon salt.

BANANA AND BLUEBERRY DELIGHT
(145 calories per serving)

1 3- or 3¼-ounce
  package regular
  vanilla-pudding
  mix
2 cups skimmed milk
  or reliquefied non-fat dry milk

1 medium banana
1 pint blueberries

ABOUT 8 HOURS BEFORE SERVING OR EARLY IN DAY:

In medium saucepan, prepare pudding mix as label directs but use skimmed milk. Cover surface with waxed paper and refrigerate just until cool. Slice banana; fold banana slices and blueberries into cooled pudding. Spoon into six dessert dishes or custard cups. Refrigerate until cold. Makes 6 servings.

PINEAPPLE FROST PIE
(120 calories per serving)

¾ cup graham-
  cracker crumbs
1 tablespoon brown
  sugar
2 tablespoons butter
  or margarine,
  melted
1 8-ounce can crushed
  pineapple in its own juice, chilled

orange juice, chilled
½ cup non-fat dry
  milk powder
1 egg white
1 tablespoon lemon
  juice
¼ cup sugar

UP TO 1 WEEK AHEAD:

In 9-inch pie plate, mix graham-cracker crumbs, brown sugar and butter or margarine. Set aside one tablespoon crumb mixture for garnish. With back of spoon, press remaining mixture to bottom and side of plate; refrigerate.

Drain pineapple, reserving juice; to pineapple juice, add orange juice to make ½ cup, if necessary. In small bowl, with mixer at high speed, beat non-fat dry milk powder, egg white and lemon juice and reserved pineapple juice mixture until soft peaks form. Slowly add sugar, beating well after each addition. Fold in drained pineapple. Pour into crumb crust; sprinkle with reserved crumb mixture. Freeze, then freezer-wrap and store in freezer to use within 1 week. Makes 8 servings.

Instead of a pie, make 18 frozen sandwiches by mounding about ¼ cup of the pineapple mixture on 36 (2½-inch square) graham crackers. Only 80 calories each.

"SLIM" BERRY CHEESECAKE
(150 calories per serving)

1 cup graham
    cracker crumbs
sugar
2 tablespoons butter
    or margarine,
    melted
2 16-ounce containers
    creamed cottage cheese

4 eggs
1 teaspoon vanilla
    extract
2 pints strawberries,
    hulled
1 pint blueberries

EARLY IN DAY:

Preheat oven to 350°F. In 10" by 2" spring-form pan, mix well graham cracker crumbs, 1 tablespoon sugar and butter or margarine. With hand, press mixture firmly to bottom of springform pan; set aside.

In covered blender container at medium speed, blend half of cottage cheese at a time, until smooth, stopping occasionally scrape container with rubber spatula. Pour in large bowl. Repeat with remaining cottage cheese.

To cottage cheese in bowl, add ¾ cup sugar and vanilla. With mixer at medium speed beat until smooth; pour mixture into springform pan. Bake 1 hour or until set. Cool in pan on wire rack. Refrigerate.

TO SERVE:

With spatula, loosen edge of cheesecake from pan; carefully remove side of spring-form pan. Arrange berries on cheesecake. Makes 16 servings.

"Slim" Berry Cheesecake

ORANGE FLUFF PIE
(110 calories per serving)

1 large orange
butter or margarine
8 gingersnaps,
  crushed
¼ cup sugar
1 envelope
  unflavored gelatin
¼ teaspoon salt

3 egg whites, at
  room temperature
½ teaspoon vanilla
  extract
½ cup nonfat
  dry-milk powder
½ cup orange juice

ABOUT 3 HOURS BEFORE SERVING:

1. Cut a thin slice from orange; reserve for garnish. Grate 1 tablespoon peel; section and cut orange into ½-inch pieces.
2. Lightly grease bottom of 9-inch pie plate with butter or margarine. Reserve 1 tablespoon crushed gingersnaps; sprinkle remaining crushed gingersnaps evenly over bottom of pie plate; set aside.
3. In 1-quart saucepan, combine sugar, gelatin and salt; stir in ½ cup cold water. Over high heat, heat mixture to boiling, stirring constantly. Reduce heat to medium; cook 5 minutes, stirring occasionally.
4. Meanwhile, in large bowl with mixer at high speed, beat egg whites until stiff peaks form. Beating at high speed, gradually pour gelatin mixture into beaten whites. Continue beating until mixture stands in stiff, glossy peaks. Beat in vanilla; set aside.
5. In small bowl with mixer at high speed, beat non-fat dry-milk powder and orange juice until stiff peaks form, about 7 minutes, occasionally scarping bowl with rubber spatula.
6. Fold whipped-milk mixture, orange peel and orange pieces into egg-white mixture until well blended; pour into pie plate and spread evenly to edge of pie plate. Refrigerate until set, about 2 hours.

TO SERVE:

Sprinkle top of pie with reserved crushed gingersnaps and garnish with orange slice. Makes 8 servings.

Fabulous!!

LIGHT PEACH BAVARIAN
(130 calories per serving)

ABOUT 2½ HOURS BEFORE SERVING OR DAY AHEAD:

In 2-quart saucepan, evenly sprinkle 1 envelope unflavored gelatin onto ½ cup water. Over medium heat, cook, stirring constantly until gelatin is dissolved; set aside.

Meanwhile, in covered blender container at high speed, puree peaches and their liquid from one 16-ounce can cling-peach halves in heavy syrup, ¼ teaspoon vanilla extract and ⅛ teaspoon salt. Stir peaches into gelatin; chill until mixture mounds when dropped from a spoon, about 2 hours.

With wire whisk, fold in ½ cup frozen whipped topping, thawed, and spoon into four individual dessert dishes. Refrigerate until set, about 1 hour. Garnish with candied violets and mint leaves. Makes 4 servings.

PEARS WITH MINT CUSTARD SAUCE
(165 calories per serving)

¼ cup sugar
1 tablespoon corn-
  starch
¼ teaspoon salt
2 cups skimmed milk
  or reliquefied non-
  fat dry milk
2 egg yolks

¼ teaspoon pepper-
  mint extract
2 29-ounce cans
  pear halves,
  drained
¼ cup coconut,
  toasted

ABOUT 2 HOURS BEFORE SERVING:

In heavy, 2-quart saucepan with wire whisk, mix well first 5 ingredients. Cook, over medium heat, stirring constantly, until sauce is slightly thickened, about 5 to 10 minutes. Remove from heat; stir in peppermint extract. Cover sauce surface with waxed paper; refrigerate until well chilled, about 1½ hours.

Spoon pear halves into dessert dishes; pour on sauce and sprinkle with toasted coconut. Makes 8 servings.

STRAWBERRY FREEZE
(150 calories per serving)

1 envelope unfla-
vored gelatin
1 quart skimmed
milk or reliquefied
nonfat dry milk
3 eggs
¾ cup sugar
2 teaspoons vanilla
extract
¼ teaspoon salt
1 pint strawberries,
chopped

ABOUT 6 HOURS BEFORE SERVING:

1. In 1-quart saucepan, evenly sprinkle gelatin onto ½ cup milk. Over medium heat, cook until gelatin is completely dissolved, stirring constantly; set aside.

2. In large bowl, with mixer at high speed, beat eggs until thick and fluffy; beating at high speed, gradually sprinkle in sugar, 2 tablespoons at a time, until sugar is completely dissolved and mixture is thick and lemon colored, about 5 minutes. Reduce speed to low; beat in remaining milk, vanilla, salt and gelatin mixture.

3. Pour mixture into 13″ × 9″ baking pan. Cover pan and freeze until frozen but still soft, about 3 hours. Spoon half of mixture into blender container; cover and blend at medium speed, until smooth but still frozen; pour mixture into a well-chilled medium bowl. Repeat with remaining half of mixture, Fold in strawberries.

4. Return mixture to baking pan; cover and freeze until firm, about 2 hours, stirring occasionally. Makes 9 servings.

ORANGE-TAPIOCA DESSERT
(80 calories per serving)

2½ cups orange
juice
¼ cup quick-
cooking tapioca
1 tablespoon brown
sugar
⅛ teaspoon ground
cinnamon
dash salt
2 teaspoons graham-
cracker crumbs

EARLY IN DAY:

In 2-quart saucepan, mix orange juice, tapioca, brown sugar, cinnamon and salt. Let stand 5 minutes. Over medium heat, heat tapioca mixture to boiling, stirring frequently. Remove from heat; let stand 20 minutes; then stir. Spoon mixture into 6 small dessert dishes refrigerate. To serve, top each dessert with some graham-cracker crumbs. Makes 6 servings.

GLAZED PINEAPPLE SPONGE CAKE
(195 calories per serving)

1 8-ounce can
crushed pineapple
in its own juice
6 eggs, separated
1½ cup sugar
1 teaspoon vanilla
extract
¼ teaspoon salt
1½ cup all-purpose
flour
¾ teaspoon cream of
tartar
Pineapple Glaze
(below)

ABOUT 4 HOURS BEFORE SERVING OR EARLY IN DAY:

Drain pineapple, reserving liquid. Preheat oven to 325°F. In large bowl, with mixer at high speed, beat egg yolks, sugar, vanilla, salt and ½ cup cold water until light and fluffy, about 2 minutes, occasionally scraping bowl with rubber spatula. Reduce speed to low; gradually sprinkle in flour, beating until blended, scraping bowl. Stir in drained pineapple. Wash and dry beaters.

In small bowl, with mixer at high speed, beat egg whites and cream of tartar until stiff peaks form. With wire whisk or rubber spatula, fold beaten whites into yolk mixture. Pour batter into ungreased 10-inch tube pan. Bake 1 hour or until top springs back when lightly touched with finger. Invert cake in pan on bottle; cool completely.

TO SERVE:

With small spatula, spread Pineapple Glaze over top and side of cake. Makes 16 servings.

PINEAPPLE GLAZE:
(45 calories per serving)

In small bowl, stir 1½ cups confectioners' sugar, 2 tablespooons reserved pineapple juice, 2 to 3 teaspoons lemon juice until of spreading consistency.

This cake is delicious without the pineapple glaze (saves 45 calories)

(Clockwise from top)
Strawberry Freeze
Glazed Pineapple Sponge Cake
Coffee Mold with Custard Sauce
Peach-Topped Cheese Cakes
Orange Fluff Pie
Pears with Mint Custard Sauce
Light Peach Bavarian

PEACH-TOPPED CHEESE CAKE
(190 calories per serving)

1 16-ounce can sliced cling peaches in light fruit juice.
1½ 8-ounce package Neufchatel cheese

2 eggs
½ cup sugar
½ teaspoon almond extract

ABOUT 3 HOURS BEFORE SERVING:

Drain peaches, reserving liquid. Set aside liquid and 8 peach slices. Place remaining peaches in eight 6-ounce custard cups.

Preheat oven to 350°F. In small bowl, with mixer at low speed, beat cheese, eggs, sugar and almond extract just until well mixed, constantly scraping bowl with rubber spatula. Increase speed to high; beat until mixture is smooth, about 1 minute, scraping bowl occasionally.

Pour cheese mixture into custard cups; bake 20 minutes or until set. Refrigerate until well chilled, about 2 hours.

TO SERVE:

Top each dessert with a peach slice and pour some reserved juice over top of cake. Makes 8 servings.

MINTED FRUIT FONDUE
(70 calories per serving)

1 medium apple, cut into chunks
1 medium pear, cut into chunks
1 medium banana, sliced
3 tablespoons lemon juice

1 tablespoon cornstarch
1 cup orange juice
⅛ teaspoon peppermint extract

ABOUT 15 MINUTES BEFORE SERVING:

In medium bowl, toss apple, pear and banana with lemon juice to prevent browing; arrange on large platter and set aside.

In small saucepan combine cornstarch, orange juice and mint extract. Over medium heat, heat mixture, stirring constantly, until thickened and bubbly; pour into fondue pot or chafing dish; place over low heat.

To serve, have guests dip fruit into hot sauce. (Provide fondue forks for dipping.) Makes 6 servings.

COFFEE MOLD WITH CUSTARD SAUCE
(115 calories per serving)

3 envelopes unflavored gelatin
sugar
4 cups strong coffee
1 tablespoon lemon juice
2 egg yolks

2 cups skimmed milk or reliquefied nonfat dry milk
1 tablespoon cornstarch
¼ teaspon salt
1 teaspoon vanilla extract

ABOUT 6½ HOURS BEFORE SERVING OR DAY AHEAD:

In 3-quart saucepan, mix gelatin and 1 cup sugar. Gradually stir in 1 cup water, then coffee. Over medium heat, cook, stirring constantly, until gelatin is completely dissolved. Remove from heat and add lemon juice. Place 6-cup ring mold in jelly-roll pan for easier handling. Carefully pour gelatin mixture into mold. Chill about 6 hours or until set. Meanwhile, prepare Custard Sauce: In heavy, 2-quart saucepan, with wire whisk, mix well egg yolks, milk, cornstarch, salt and ¼ cup sugar. Over medium heat, cook, stirring constantly, until mixture is slightly thickened, about 7 minutes. Remove from heat; stir in vanilla. Cover sauce surface with waxed paper; refrigerate until well chilled, about 2 hours.

TO SERVE:

Unmold gelatin onto chilled dessert plate; serve sauce in small bowl in center of mold. Makes 12 servings.

minted fruit fondue makes a fun party dish

NOTES & RECIPES